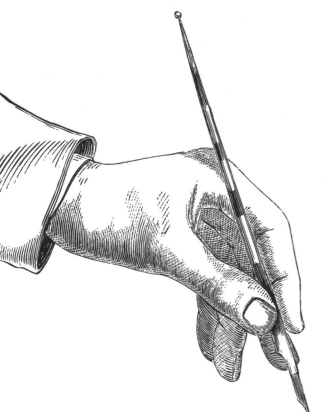

This book belongs to:

_____

LEARN Cursive
WITH
JOKES

Seaside Study

TABLE OF CONTENTS

Introduction

Welcome to a cursive handwriting journey like no other! In this unique handwriting joke book, we embark on a quest to not only improve your penmanship but to add a dash of humor and creativity along the way. We'll start with essential handwriting tips and advice, setting the foundation for your progress. Then, you'll delve into letter practice to hone your skills. But here's the twist: we'll sprinkle in short jokes to keep you entertained and engaged. And for the grand finale, we'll challenge you with long riddles to write, fostering both your handwriting finesse and your sense of humor. Get ready to master the art of writing with a grin and a giggle!

Tips from the Pros!

1. Posture Matters

Sit up straight with both feet flat on the ground. Good posture supports proper alignment of your hand and wrist, making it easier to control your movements.

2. Relax Your Grip

Hold your pen or pencil gently, with your fingers forming a tripod grip (thumb and two fingers). Avoid gripping too tightly, which can lead to fatigue and cramped fingers.

3. Consistency is Key

Strive for consistent letter size and spacing. This uniformity makes your handwriting more legible and aesthetically pleasing.

4. Sloped Writing

Angle your paper slightly to the left if you're right-handed and to the right if you're left-handed. This allows your hand to move more freely and reduces smudging.

5. Practice Letter Formation

Pay attention to how each letter is formed. Consistent and correct letter formation is vital for legibility. Utilize lined paper to help with letter height and spacing.

6. Slow Down

Take your time when writing. Rushing can lead to sloppy handwriting. As you practice, you'll naturally become faster without sacrificing quality.

7. Use the Right Tools

Choose a pen or pencil that feels comfortable in your hand. Experiment with different writing instruments until you find the one that suits you best.

8. Warm-Up Exercises

Before you begin writing, do a few warm-up exercises to loosen your hand and wrist. Simple doodles and loops on your paper can help prepare your muscles for writing.

9. Patience and Perseverance

Remember that improving your handwriting takes time. Be patient with yourself and don't get discouraged by initial challenges.

10. Seek Feedback

Ask friends, family, or teachers to review your handwriting and offer constructive feedback. Sometimes an outside perspective can help identify areas for improvement.

Chapter 1

In this chapter, we'll dive into the basics, the building blocks of beautiful cursive-handwriting drills and letter formation. Just like stretching before a race, these warm-up exercises are crucial to prepare your hand and mind for the exciting adventure ahead. So, grab your favorite pen or pencil, and let's get started on the path to impeccable penmanship!

Let's get started.

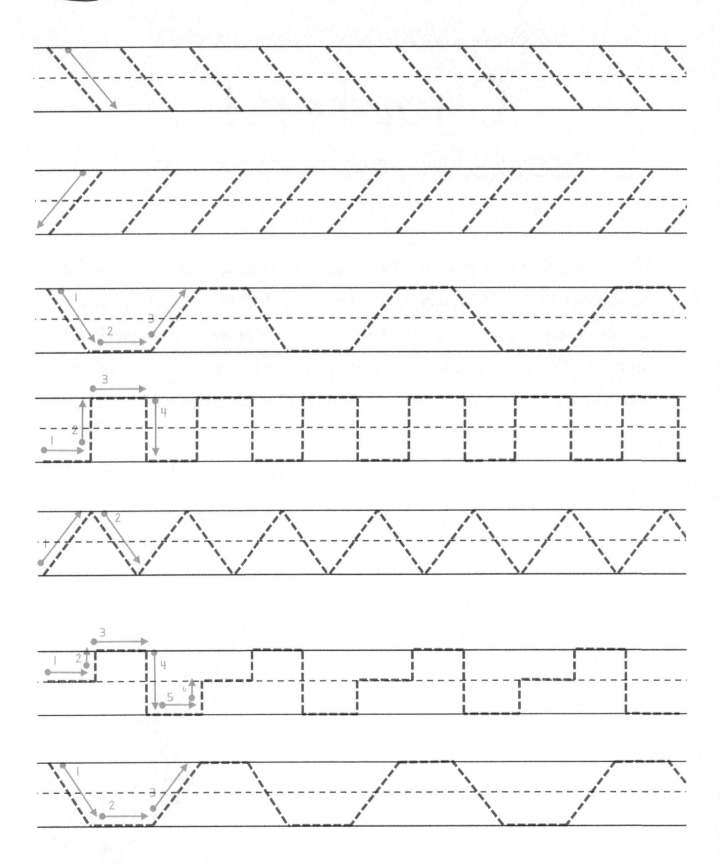

6

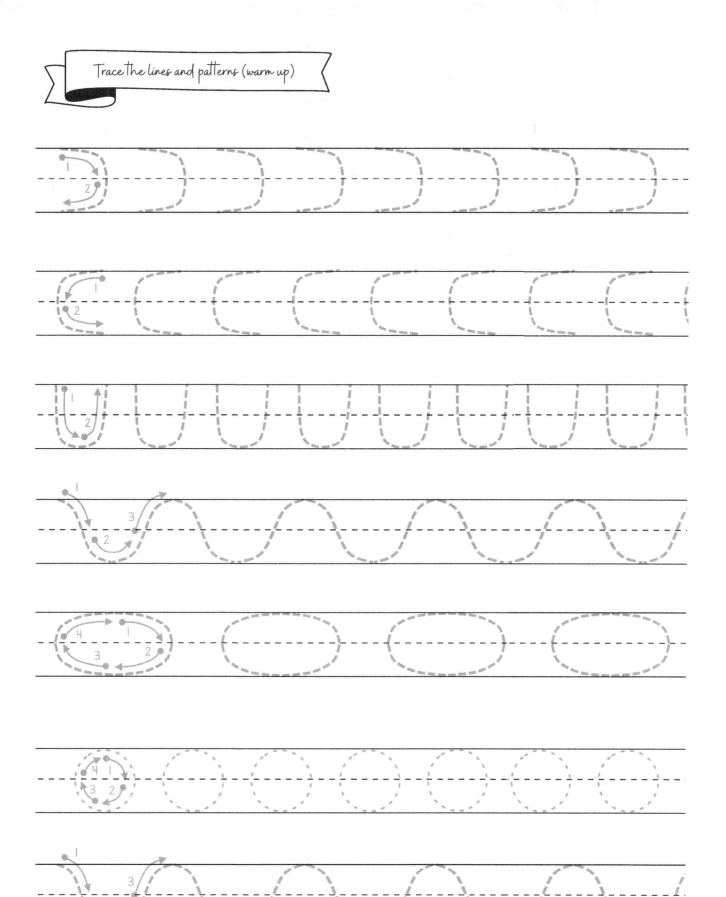

7

Cursive Alphabet

A B C D E F G

H I J K L M

N O P Q R S T

U V V W X Y Z

a b c d e f g h i

j k l m n o p q r

s t u v w x y z

8

Áâ

á a a a a a a

a a a a a a a

a

Á a a a a a a

a a a a a a

a

A B C D E F G H I J K L M N O P Q R S T U V W X Y Z

9

B b

h   h   h   h   h   h   h

h   h   h   h   h   h   h

h

B   B   B   B   B   B   B

B   B   B   B   B   B   B

B

A B C D E F G H I J K L M N O P Q R S T U V W X Y Z

10

c c c c c c c c c

c c c c c c c c c

c

C C C C C C C

C C C C C C C

C

A B C D E F G H I J K L M N O P Q R S T U V W X Y Z

$\mathcal{D}\,d$

d d d d d d d

d d d d d d d

d

$\mathcal{D}$ $\mathcal{D}$ $\mathcal{D}$ $\mathcal{D}$ $\mathcal{D}$

$\mathcal{D}$ $\mathcal{D}$ $\mathcal{D}$ $\mathcal{D}$ $\mathcal{D}$

$\mathcal{D}$

A B C **D** E F G H I J K L M N O P Q R S T U V W X Y Z

_E e_

e   e   e   e   e   e   e   e

e   e   e   e   e   e   e   e

e

E   E   E   E   E   E   E

E   E   E   E   E   E   E

E

A B C D **E** F G H I J K L M N O P Q R S T U V W X Y Z

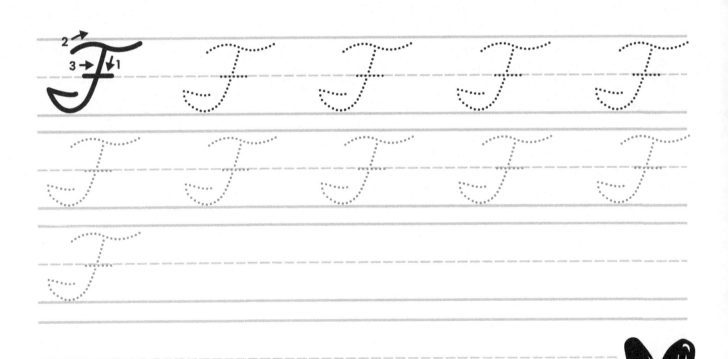

A B C D E **F** G H I J K L M N O P Q R S T U V W X Y Z

G g

g g g g g g g g

g g g g g g g

g

G G G G G

G G G G G

G

RING RING

A B C D E F G H I J K L M N O P Q R S T U V W X Y Z

15

H h

h   h   h   h   h   h   h

h   h   h   h   h   h   h

h

H   H   H   H   H   H

H   H   H   H   H   H   H

H

A B C D E F G H I J K L M N O P Q R S T U V W X Y Z

Ii

i i i i i i i i i

i i i i i i i i i

i

I I I I I

I I I I I

I

A B C D E F G H **I** J K L M N O P Q R S T U V W X Y Z

17

A B C D E F G H I J K L M N O P Q R S T U V W X Y Z

K k

k   k   k   k   k   k   k

k   k   k   k   k   k   k

k

K   K   K   K   K   K

K   K   K   K   K   K

K

A B C D E F G H I J K L M N O P Q R S T U V W X Y Z

$\mathcal{Ll}$

ℓ ℓ ℓ ℓ ℓ ℓ ℓ ℓ

ℓ ℓ ℓ ℓ ℓ ℓ ℓ ℓ

ℓ

$\mathcal{L}$ $\mathcal{L}$ $\mathcal{L}$ $\mathcal{L}$ $\mathcal{L}$ $\mathcal{L}$

$\mathcal{L}$ $\mathcal{L}$ $\mathcal{L}$ $\mathcal{L}$ $\mathcal{L}$ $\mathcal{L}$

$\mathcal{L}$

A B C D E F G H I J K **L** M N O P Q R S T U V W X Y Z

M m

m m m m m m m

m m m m m m

m

M m m m m m

m m m m m

m

A B C D E F G H I J K L M N O P Q R S T U V W X Y Z

$\mathcal{N}n$

n n n n n n

n n n n n

n

$\mathcal{N}$ $\mathcal{N}$ $\mathcal{N}$ $\mathcal{N}$ $\mathcal{N}$ $\mathcal{N}$

$\mathcal{N}$ $\mathcal{N}$ $\mathcal{N}$ $\mathcal{N}$ $\mathcal{N}$

$\mathcal{N}$

A B C D E F G H I J K L M N O P Q R S T U V W X Y Z

O o

O o o o o o

o o o o o o o

o

O O O O O O

O O O O O O

O

A B C D E F G H I J K L M N O P Q R S T U V W X Y Z

23

P p

p p p p p p

p p p p p p

p

P P P P P P

P P P P P P

P

A B C D E F G H I J K L M N O P Q R S T U V W X Y Z

24

2q

q

2

R r

r r r r r r r r r r

r r r r r r r r r r

r

R R R R R R

R R R R R R

R

A B C D E F G H I J K L M N O P Q R S T U V W X Y Z

26

S s

A B C D E F G H I J K L M N O P Q R S T U V W X Y Z

27

t t t t t t t t

t t t t t t t t

t

T T T T T

T T T T T

T

Stay FOCUS

A B C D E F G H I J K L M N O P Q R S T U V W X Y Z

𝒰 𝓊

𝒰 𝓊 𝓊 𝓊 𝓊 𝓊 𝓊 𝓊

𝓊 𝓊 𝓊 𝓊 𝓊 𝓊 𝓊

𝓊

𝒰 𝒰 𝒰 𝒰 𝒰 𝒰 𝒰

𝒰 𝒰 𝒰 𝒰 𝒰 𝒰 𝒰

𝒰

A B C D E F G H I J K L M N O P Q R S T U V W X Y Z

29

𝒱 𝓊

𝓊 𝓊 𝓊 𝓊 𝓊 𝓊 𝓊

𝓊 𝓊 𝓊 𝓊 𝓊 𝓊 𝓊 𝓊 𝓊 𝓊

𝓊

𝒱 𝒱 𝒱 𝒱 𝒱 𝒱

𝒱 𝒱 𝒱 𝒱 𝒱 𝒱 𝒱

𝒱

A B C D E F G H I J K L M N O P Q R S T U V W X Y Z

$\mathcal{U}$ u

u u u u u u

u u u u u u

u

$\mathcal{W}$ u u u

u u u u

u

A B C D E F G H I J K L M N O P Q R S T U V W X Y Z

31

𝑥 𝑥 𝑥 𝑥 𝑥 𝑥

𝑥 𝑥 𝑥 𝑥 𝑥 𝑥

𝑥

𝑋 𝑋 𝑋 𝑋 𝑋 𝑋

𝑋 𝑋 𝑋 𝑋 𝑋 𝑋

𝑋

A B C D E F G H I J K L M N O P Q R S T U V W X Y Z

Y y

Y y y y y y y y y y y

y y y y y y y y y y y

y

Y Y Y Y Y Y Y Y Y Y

Y Y Y Y Y Y Y Y Y

Y

dream

A B C D E F G H I J K L M N O P Q R S T U V W X Y Z

Zz

Z

Z

ABCDEFGHIJKLMNOPQRSTUVWXY**Z**

Chapter 2

Jokes

Welcome to Chapter 2 of our cursive handwriting book, where the pen meets humor! Get ready for a dose of laughter as we explore the fun side of learning to write. In this chapter, we'll provide you with short jokes to trace and write, giving your handwriting skills a delightful twist. Not only will you be mastering the art of penmanship, but you'll also have some side-splitting jokes up your sleeve. So, grab your pen, prepare to giggle, and let's dive into the world of hilarious handwriting practice!

Let's have some fun!

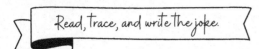

What do you call a dinosaur that is sleeping?

A dino-snore!

Trace the joke

What do you call a
dinosaur that is
sleeping?

A dino- snore!

Write the joke

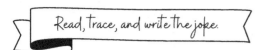
Why could the bicycle not stand up by itself?

It was two-tired!

Trace the joke

Why could the bicycle not stand up by itself?

It was two-tired!

Write the joke

39

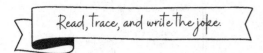

Trace the joke

Why was the math book sad?

Because it had too many problems!

Write the joke

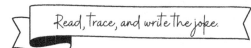

Read, trace, and write the joke.

What did one ocean say to the other ocean?

Nothing, it just waved!

Trace the joke

What did one ocean

say to the other ocean?

Nothing, it just

waved!

Write the joke

Why did the elephant bring a suitcase to the zoo?

It wanted to pack its trunk!

Trace the joke

Why did the elephant bring a suitcase to the zoo?

It wanted to pack its trunk!

Write the joke

Why do we never tell secrets on a farm?

Because the corn has ears!

Trace the joke

Why do we never tell secrets on a farm?

Because the corn has ears!

Write the joke

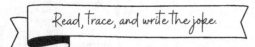

What do you call a sleeping bull? A bull-dozer!

Trace the joke

What do you call a sleeping bull?

A bull - dozer!

Write the joke

Read, trace, and write the joke.

What do you call fake spaghetti? An impasta!

Trace the joke

What do you call fake spaghetti?

An impasta!

Write the joke

45

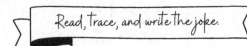

Trace the joke

Why did the scarecrow win an award?

He was outstanding in his field.

Write the joke

Trace the joke

Why do bees have sticky hair?

Because they always use honeycombs!

Write the joke

47

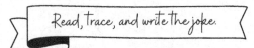
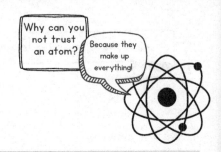

Trace the joke

Why can you not
trust an atom?

Because they make up
everything!

Write the joke

Why did the cow go to space?

To see the moooon!

Trace the joke

Why did the cow go
to space?

To see the moooon!

Write the joke

Trace the joke

What did the zero say
to the eight?

Nice belt!

Write the joke

Trace the joke

What do you call a dinosaur with an extensive vocabulary?

A thesaurus!

Write the joke

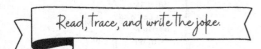

Why do birds fly south for the winter? It's too far to walk!

Trace the joke

Why do birds south for the winter?

It is too far to walk!

Write the joke

Read, trace, and write the joke.

Trace the joke

How do you make a hot dog stand?

Take away its chair!

Write the joke

53

Why can you not play hide-and-seek with mountains?

They're always peaking!

Trace the joke

Why can you not play hide - and - seek with mountains?

They are always peaking!

Write the joke

Read, trace, and write the joke.

Why was the king only a foot tall? Because he was a ruler.

Trace the joke

Why was the king only a foot tall?

Because he was a ruler!

Write the joke

55

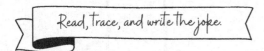

Read, trace, and write the joke.

How can you go surfing in the kitchen?

On a micro-wave!

Trace the joke

How can you go surfing in the kitchen?

On a micro- wave!

Write the joke

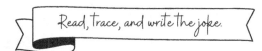

Trace the joke

How can you keep
someone in suspense?

I will tell you later!

Write the joke

Why did the golfer wear two pairs of pants?

In case he got a hole in one.

Trace the joke

Why did the golfer wear two pairs of pants?

In case he got a hole in one!

Write the joke

58

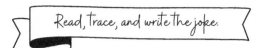

Read, trace, and write the joke.

Why was the science teacher angry?

He was a mad scientist!

Trace the joke

Why was the science teacher angry?

He was a mad scientist!

Write the joke

Why do flamingos stand on one leg?

If they lifted the other leg, they'd fall over.

Trace the joke

Why do flamingos stand on one leg?

If they lifted the other leg, they'd fall over!

Write the joke

How are fish and music the same?

They both have scales.

Trace the joke

How are fish and
music the same?

They both have
scales!

Write the joke

What is as
big as an
elephant but
weighs
zero
pounds?

The
elephants
shadow.

Read, trace, and write the joke.

Trace the joke

What is as big as an
elephant but weighs
zero pounds ?

The elephants shadow?

Write the joke

62

Trace the joke

Why did the bird go
to the library?

It was looking for
bookworms!

Write the joke

63

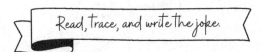

What is a bats motto?

Hang in there.

Trace the joke

What is a bats motto?

Hang in there!

Write the joke

64

What do dogs and trees have in common!

They both have bark

Trace the joke

What do dogs and trees have in common?

They both have bark!

Write the joke

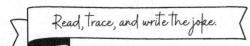

Why did
the
turkey
cross the
road!

To prove it
wasn't a
chicken.

Trace the joke

Why did the turkey cross the road?

To prove it wasn't a chicken!

Write the joke

66

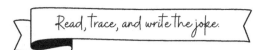

Read, trace, and write the joke.

What kind of bugs read the dictionary?

Spelling bees

Trace the joke

What kind of bugs
read the dictionary?

Spelling bees!

Write the joke

Chapter 3

Riddles

Welcome to Chapter 3 of our cursive handwriting adventure! In this section, we're taking your writing skills to the next level by adding a dash of mystery and mirth. Here, you'll find funny riddles to trace and then craft on your own. These witty challenges aren't just brain-teasers; they're also fantastic tools for honing your ability to write longer passages with grace and style. So, grab your trusty pen and prepare for a journey of laughs, riddles, and eloquent penmanship. Let's dive into the art of turning chuckles into beautifully written words!

Riddle Me This,
Write Me That

Trace the riddle

I have a shiny coat
of black and white,
and I love to
waddle around in the
cold. My favorite
food is fish, and I
sometimes slide on
my belly to get
where I want to go.

What animal am I?

Write the riddle

Answer: A penguin

Trace the riddle

I am tall when I
am young, and I
can stretch and bend
without breaking.
People often find me
in the most colorful
places, and I love
to sway in the
breeze.

What am I?

Write the riddle

Answer: A flower

Trace the riddle

I have a long, bushy tail and a mask-like pattern on my face. I'm known for being crafty and sneaky, and I love to climb trees.

What animal am I?

Write the riddle and check your answer.

Write the riddle

Answer: A raccoon

Trace the riddle

I am made of metal
and have hands, but
I can't move on
my own. People
often use me to tell
the time, and I
chime with a
pleasant sound.

What am I?

Write the riddle

Answer: A clock

Trace the riddle

I am a type of vehicle that travels on tracks, and I carry both passengers and freight. People often use me for long journeys, and I am known for my distinct " choo- choo " sound.

What am I?

Write the riddle and check your answer.

Write the riddle

Answer: A train

Trace the riddle

I am a place filled
with books of all
kinds, and people
come to borrow them
for a while. You can
find stories and
knowledge here, and
I am often a quiet
and peaceful space.

What location am I?

Write the riddle

Answer: A library

Trace the riddle

I am a creature with wings, and I am often associated with magical stories. People believe I grant wishes, and I leave a trail of sparkling dust wherever I go.

Who am I?

Write the riddle

Answer: A fairy

Trace the riddle

I am a delicious
treat that comes in
many flavors and
colors. People enjoy
licking me on hot
days, and I can
sometimes be served
in a cone or
a cup.

What am I?

Write the riddle and check your answer.

Write the riddle

Answer: Ice cream

Trace the riddle

I am a game played
on a large green
field, and I
involve hitting a
small white ball
with a club. People
try to get the ball
into a series of holes
using the least
number of strokes.

What sport am I?

Write the riddle and check your answer.

Write the riddle

Answer: Golf

Trace the riddle

I am a season that comes after summer, and I bring falling leaves and cooler weather. People often dress up in costumes and go trick-or-treating during this time.

What season am I?

Write the riddle

Answer: Autumn

Chapter 4

Free Writing

Welcome to the creative heart of our handwriting book - Chapter 4! Here, we give you the space to let your imagination run wild. It's your chance to practice cursive handwriting and, more importantly, to craft your own jokes and riddles. Think of it as a playground for your pen, where the rules are flexible, and the only limit is your own creativity. So, grab your pen and let your thoughts flow onto the page. This chapter is all about exploring your unique voice and giving life to your very own humor and wit. Let's embark on this exciting journey to create, laugh, and pen your way to handwriting mastery!

Aa Bb Cc Dd Ee Ff Gg Hh Ii Jj Kk Ll Mm Nn Oo Pp Qq Rr Ss Tt Uu Vv Ww Xx Yy Zz

Aa Bb Cc Dd Ee Ff Gg Hh Ii Jj Kk Ll Mm Nn Oo Pp Qq Rr Ss Tt Uu Vv Ww Xx Yy Zz

93

Aa Bb Cc Dd Ee Ff Gg Hh Ii Jj Kk Ll Mm Nn Oo Pp Qq Rr Ss Tt Uu Vv Ww Xx Yy Zz

Aa Bb Cc Dd Ee Ff Gg Hh Ii Jj Kk Ll Mm Nn Oo Pp Qq Rr Ss Tt Uu Vv Ww Xx Yy Zz

Aa Bb Cc Dd Ee Ff Gg Hh Ii Jj Kk Ll Mm Nn Oo Pp Qq Rr Ss Tt Uu Vv Ww Xx Yy Zz

Aa Bb Cc Dd Ee Ff Gg Hh Ii Jj Kk Ll Mm Nn Oo Pp Qq Rr Ss Tt Uu Vv Ww Xx Yy Zz

Aa Bb Cc Dd Ee Ff Gg Hh Ii Jj Kk Ll Mm Nn Oo Pp Qq Rr Ss Tt Uu Vv Ww Xx Yy Zz

Aa Bb Cc Dd Ee Ff Gg Hh Ii Jj Kk Ll Mm Nn Oo Pp Qq Rr Ss Tt Uu Vv Ww Xx Yy Zz

Aa Bb Cc Dd Ee Ff Gg Hh Ii Jj Kk Ll Mm Nn Oo Pp Qq Rr Ss Tt Uu Vv Ww Xx Yy Zz

Aa Bb Cc Dd Ee Ff Gg Hh Ii Jj Kk Ll Mm Nn Oo Pp Qq Rr Ss Tt Uu Vv Ww Xx Yy Zz

Aa Bb Cc Dd Ee Ff Gg Hh Ii Jj Kk Ll Mm Nn Oo Pp Qq Rr Ss Tt Uu Vv Ww Xx Yy Zz

Aa Bb Cc Dd Ee Ff Gg Hh Ii Jj Kk Ll Mm Nn Oo Pp Qq Rr Ss Tt Uu Vv Ww Xx Yy Zz

Made in the USA
Coppell, TX
03 March 2024